To Seth

I hope ~~you~~ ~~enjoy learning~~

about Science and Engineering...

Best Wishes

C.W. 2013

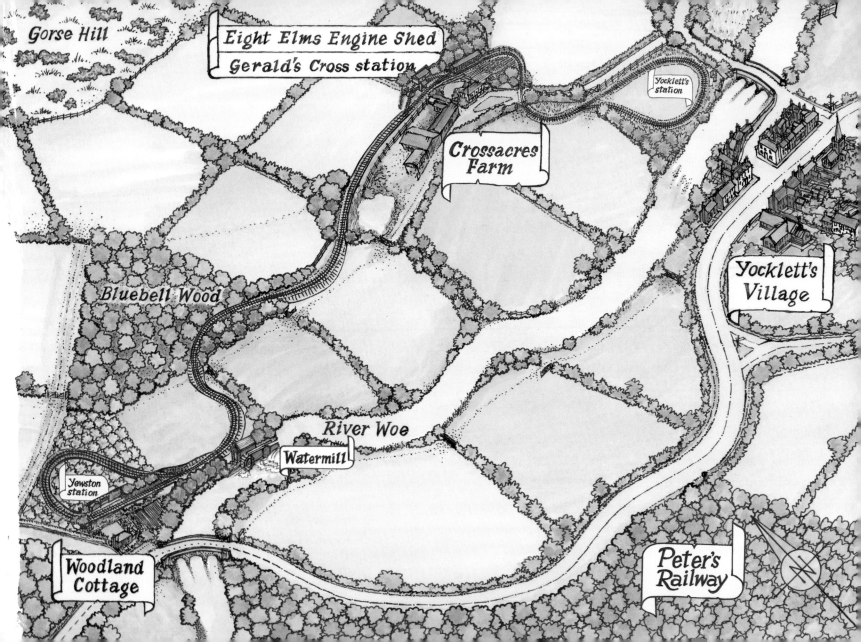

Gorse Hill

Eight Elms Engine Shed

Gerald's Cross station

Yocklett's station

Crossacres Farm

Bluebell Wood

Yocklett's Village

River Woe

Watermill

Yewston station

Woodland Cottage

Peter's Railway

Peter's Railway to the Rescue 4

Published by Christopher Vine 2010

Printed by The Amadeus Press
Cleckheaton, West Yorkshire,
England.

ISBN 978-0-9553359-4-5

Foreword

My fascination with engineering started at a very early age, solving practical problems first by watching and then helping my dad. Getting interested and excited by cars, planes, lorries and trains and playing with Lego and Meccano led on to fixing toys, bicycles, lawnmowers, motorbikes and cars.

Wondering why things work and then figuring it out gives great satisfaction. Having a truly hands-on approach is really important in developing our future engineers and scientists. Encouraging young people to acquire the skills required by being excited is key to this.

These books show children that it really can be fun to work with mechanical objects whilst keeping an eye on issues regarding the environment and sustainability. Only technology will resolve the dilemmas surrounding these problems.

I think Chris' books present engineering and scientific principles in an imaginative yet educational storyline and I hope they will capture the imagination of our future engineers.

Colin P Smith. Director of Engineering & Technology, Rolls Royce plc.

Rolls Royce plc is the most famous engineering company in the world. Colin Smith, as the Chief Engineer, is responsible for the safety, design, and technology of jet engines for aeroplanes, gas turbines for ships, electricity power stations, nuclear reactors, diesel engines and many other engineering wonders.

The watercolour illustrations are by John Wardle.

The Big Freeze

The adventures on Peter's Railway have usually taken place on warm sunny days in the summer. But now the days are short and the nights are long. It is the middle of winter.

Peter and his family live at Woodland Cottage in a pretty valley in the countryside. The house is beside the River Woe and living there with Peter are his Mum and Dad, Jo and Colin and the twins, Kitty and Harry. They are much younger than Peter but are now becoming quite useful, or getting up to mischief; in about equal measure.

The nearest house to Woodland Cottage is Crossacres Farm. It is about half a mile away, across some fields and the other side of Bluebell Wood. Grandpa Gerald and Grandma Pat have lived there for many years and when Grandpa isn't busy farming, he can usually be found in his workshop, making things.

When Peter and Grandpa Gerald first built their railway, it was a simple up and down line, linking their houses across the fields. They built it so they could visit each other by train as Grandpa doesn't own a car and it's too far to walk along the winding country road.

Since then the railway has changed quite a bit. First they added a turntable and turning loop so the trains didn't have to go backwards for the return trips. Then they extended the line beyond Crossacres Farm, all the way to Yockletts Village for Grandma to do her shopping. (And for racing trains!)

When they built the line, Mr Esmond had lent them Fiery Fox to pull the trains. Fiery Fox is a beautiful and very powerful steam locomotive, painted a wonderful shade of apple green.

One day Grandpa and Peter would like to build their own locomotive, but it had taken Mr Esmond eight years to build Fiery Fox. So for the time being, building their own engine is a good dream for the future..... But back to the present.

This winter was the coldest anyone could remember and the snow lay on the ground without melting for days on end. At night the temperature fell to -15°C and during the day it did not often get above freezing.

For the highland cows and sheep on Grandpa's farm, the cold wasn't too uncomfortable, as their woolly coats kept them perfectly warm. They were also in the field next to Bluebell Wood, where they could take shelter under the trees. Their real problem was hunger, because the grass was buried under the snow.

To help out during a school holiday, Peter had gone to stay at the farm. Every day he and Grandpa loaded bales of hay and buckets of rolled barley onto a flat trailer. Then they towed it to the field with the tractor.

One morning, looking at the outside thermometer, they saw the temperature had plunged to the lowest yet: -20°C. This was the same temperature as inside Grandma's freezer and not much warmer than the Arctic.

They dressed up even more warmly than usual and set off to load the trailer. All was going well until Grandpa tried to start the tractor. It didn't matter how much he tried, it just would not go. The battery was in good condition and the starter motor churned the engine over and over, but it wouldn't fire up. It was as dead as a dodo. It took Grandpa a while to work out what was wrong, but then he realised.

"You know what has happened?" he asked Peter. "It's so cold that the diesel fuel has frozen solid in the pipes and won't flow. We'll have to think of a different plan for feeding the animals today."

"Do you think," wondered Peter out loud, "that Fiery Fox could make it through the snow? The railway runs right through their field and next to the troughs. We could deliver everything by rail."

Grandpa thought about it for a minute or two. "The trouble is you can't even see the track through the snow," he said at last. "If we can't get through, we'll have wasted too much time messing about. I'm afraid we will have to think of something else."

Peter wasn't so easily put off. The idea of driving the engine through the snow was too exciting. "Could we build a snow plough?" he suggested. "Do you think we could make one quickly enough?"

"Hmmm, maybe," laughed Grandpa, who could see that Peter was not going to be so easily deflected from his plan.

"Perhaps we could make some sort of a plough by using one of the heavy bogie wagons. The only difficult part would be to make the curved blades which cut into the snow."

After a bit more thinking, Grandpa wandered off to the tractor shed and disappeared inside. He was looking for something.

"I've found just what we need," he shouted, coming back out of the shed with two bits of metal. "These are spare mole boards from the farm plough."

They were the curved metal plates which turn the soil over as the plough is pulled through the ground. They would make the perfect scoops or blades for a miniature railway snow plough. Grandpa's idea was to fix them onto the front of one of their wagons with a strong metal frame.

Up at the engine shed, they decided to use the engineers' wagon because it was very heavy and, helpfully, it was at the front of the shed, just inside the door.

They pushed it along the line and into the workshop, through the double doors and got to work. No time to light the stove to warm them up, there was too much to do and they were in a hurry.

The first thing to make was a frame from some old pieces of angle iron. It was quite simple, the bits of metal just needed cutting to length and some holes drilled for bolting it to the end of the wagon.

Then they held the two mole boards up against the frame and drew lines on them, showing where to trim their ends so they would fit together in a 'V' shape at the front. A few more minutes' hard work with the hack saw, and they were ready to bolt the mole boards into place. Sawing the metal by hand was hard work, but at least it had warmed them up!

Once bolted on, the blades were held just a few millimetres above the track. They made a sort of arrow shape which would cut into the snow and push it to the sides. If they

went fast enough, the curve in the blades would tend to lift and throw the snow. It was perfect.

There was no time to sit around and admire it though; the animals were hungry. They pushed the new snow plough out of the workshop and backed it onto Fiery Fox and coupled up.

They were nearly ready to light the fire and get up steam, but there was one vital job to do.

At the beginning of winter, Grandpa had drained all the water out of the boiler. He did not want the water to freeze into a solid block of ice and burst it open.

They would need to fill it up, but the water tower was frozen and so was the hose pipe. There was nothing for it but to fetch buckets of water from the kitchen.

Peter watched the water gauges in the cab so they could get the water level in the boiler just right. Finally they poured several more bucketfuls into the tender and they were ready for action.

Dropping a firelighter into the firebox, Peter lit it with a long match. Then he pushed in some dry sticks and bigger bits of wood. Soon the fire was crackling away and some lumps of coal were added on top.

The heat from the fire was spreading through the boiler; Fiery Fox was coming to life.

Usually if there was a steam-up, Minnie and Cato would be on parade, inspecting the proceedings, or dozing in the sun. But they weren't stupid. Today they were in the sitting room, curled up in front of the blazing log fire.

While Peter filled all the oil boxes on the engine, Grandpa filled the tender with a good supply of coal.

As the pressure slowly came up, they made some more preparations.

"What we need to do now," Grandpa explained, "is put some heavy concrete blocks in the wagon part of the plough. They will do two things: first, they will hold it down and keep it on the rails. But they will also give it extra mass and momentum to help it punch through any deep drifts."

There was a little stack of blocks just behind the shed, so they lifted some in. Peter then coupled up some more wagons behind the engine, to make the whole train even more like a battering ram.

Then they loaded up the wagons with bales of hay, some straw and buckets of rolled barley. That would keep the animals fed and comfortable for another day. Finally they put on a small churn of milk for Woodland Cottage.

By the time they had loaded everything on, the pressure gauge was showing the boiler at working pressure and they were ready.

Charge the Drift!

Peter opened the cylinder drains and cracked open the regulator to allow a little steam from the boiler to go to the cylinders to warm them up. They certainly needed it today. Steam poured out of the drain pipes and drifted out of the shed.

Once Grandpa was on the guard's van at the back, Peter released the brakes and opened the regulator a little more.

Fiery Fox wheezed forwards and steam went everywhere. Usually on the hot summer days, it cleared away quickly. But today it hung around and looked spectacular. Even their breath made clouds in front of their faces.

Anyone who had been watching the train ease out of the shed and onto the line would have noticed how purposeful it looked. But would it be powerful enough to clear the snow?

There was a layer of snow covering the line and Peter drove slowly and carefully. The cylinders were hot now and he closed the drains.

Fiery Fox propelled the plough with great force and the plough pushed the snow to either side of the track. The last tiny bit of snow on the tops of the rails was squashed or pushed out of the way by the wheels.

By the time the train had passed, you could see two dark lines in the snow; the steel rails. The sleepers and ballast were still completely covered.

Passing the frozen duck pond, Peter opened the regulator a bit more and they picked up speed.

The plough was now clearing the snow quite easily as they went through the first field. In fact, by going faster, the curved shape of the blades was starting to lift the snow and throw it. This took less force than just pushing it to one side and compressing it into a solid bank.

After the field, the line wound its way through Bluebell Wood. There was hardly any snow under the trees and Fiery Fox had an easy job. However as they came round the curve to leave the wood, Peter saw a dreadful sight in front of him.

The cutting in the field ahead was filled up with snow, almost to the top. Peter flung open the regulator to give Fiery Fox full power. Her exhaust barked up the chimney and she threw up a great shower of sparks as the fire was pulled through the boiler to make more steam.

She surged ahead, pushing the plough in front and charged at the snow drift.

Snow went everywhere. Sideways, up in the air and right over the top of the engine. Peter couldn't see a thing. The wheels were slipping on the rails; the snow was just too heavy. They were slowing down. Slower.... slower.... stuck.

"Are you alright back there?" shouted Peter over his shoulder.

"No problem," called back Grandpa. "You'll just have to back her out and charge the drift again."

Peter wound the reverser into reverse gear and tried a bit of steam. Fiery Fox's wheels spun backwards on the slippery rails, but after a few seconds they seemed to find some grip.

Very slowly the train backed up the track and into the wood. They were ready for another go.

"Charge!" shouted Grandpa from the rear.

Peter whistled, opened the regulator and charged the drift again. They didn't get right through, but they had made some progress.

"We'll just have to do it again," he shouted back to Grandpa.

And so, bit by bit they attacked the snow drift in the cutting until they had only a few metres to go.

This time they reversed the train further up the line, for a longer run up, to hit it really fast.

Peter put more coal on the fire, checked the water level and called over his shoulder, "The final assault!" Then, with a long blast on the whistle, he put on steam.

Fiery Fox hauled on the train, pushed on the heavy snow plough and accelerated rapidly. By the time she left the woods and got onto the straight, she was going like a bullet.

Charging through the cleared part of the cutting, they slammed into the drift at the end. The whole train shook with the impact but hardly slowed at all. This time the snow couldn't stop them and they exploded out of the cutting in a huge spray of snow.

Peter wasn't going to stop now and he kept on right across the field. He only shut off steam when they got to the feed and water troughs for the animals.

By now, the animals had seen the train heading towards them, loaded with food. The cows galloped over and started to eat the hay while it was still moving, trotting along beside it. Then the sheep arrived and tried to get their heads in the moving buckets. It was total chaos, mayhem, pandemonium, call it what you like.

When they had stopped and unloaded everything, Grandpa checked the water trough. Of course the water had frozen on top so he broke up the ice. But the supply pipe had frozen too.

"Never mind," he said. "I've a cunning plan to fix that. We'll thaw it out with straw..."

Peter couldn't see how straw would melt the water in the pipe, but he didn't say so. Grandpa was a wise old bird and probably had some sort of trick up his sleeve.

Peter watched as Grandpa picked up some of the straw and packed it around the metal pipe, where it came out of the ground. Then, striking a match he lit it and waited patiently while the flames heated up the pipe and the ice inside. It wasn't long before there was a satisfying gurgle and the water started to flow again.

The animals wouldn't be hungry or thirsty tonight.

Climbing back on the train, Peter drove on down the line to Woodland Cottage. It was mostly downhill and the plough made light work of clearing the snow.

After delivering the churn of milk to his mum, they had a lovely journey back to the farm. It was easy now and they could enjoy looking at the scenery under its white blanket of snow. The animals didn't even look up when they passed. They were much too busy scoffing and drinking!

Back at the shed, it was time to let Fiery Fox's fire go out and drain her boiler again.

"We'll blow the boiler down whilst there is still some pressure," said Grandpa as they wiped her down with dusters and polish. "That will make sure it's empty before there's the slightest chance of freezing."

Opening the boiler blow-down valves, there was a great rushing noise from under the engine, as the pressure in the boiler blew all the water out. It turned to steam in the air and after a few seconds they couldn't see a thing. They were in the middle of a cloud.

Then quite suddenly, the boiler was empty and with a final hiss of steam, all went quiet. They pushed Fiery Fox and the train backwards into the shed and locked the door for the night.

"That was quite some day," said Peter, as they went in for a cup of tea. "It was hard work and cold, but I wouldn't have missed it for anything."

"Neither would I," chuckled Grandpa. "I have always wanted to see a railway snow plough charging a drift. But I never thought I would be riding behind one, being chased by cows."

The Snow Plough

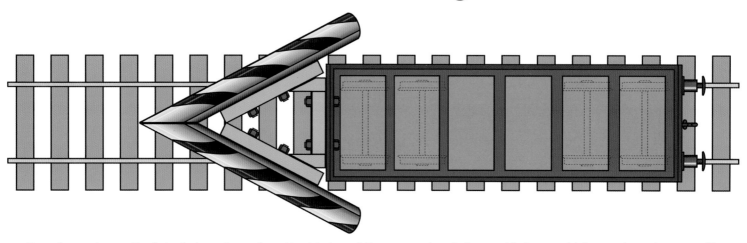

Seen from above, the 'plan' view shows how the blades of the snow plough form a V shape which cuts into the snow like a knife. The plough is bolted (red) to the engineers' wagon with a very strong metal frame (green).

On the outside of the blades, the heads of the bolts are level or 'flush' with the smooth surface so that the blades slide easily through the snow.

The grey rectangular shapes in the snow plough are concrete blocks. They are very heavy and their 'mass' helps the plough to punch through snow drifts like a heavy hammer. Their weight also holds the plough firmly down on the track.

The blades are held just above the top of the rails. Any snow which goes under them, is pushed out of the way by the wheels.

Seen from the side, the scoop shape of the blades is clearly visible. As they cut into the snow, it is both lifted and thrown outwards. The four red circles are the smooth heads of the bolts which hold the blades to the frame.

Ice - Why does it Float and Burst Boilers?

When water freezes, it turns into ice.
Most things get smaller when they get colder. But water is strange and gets bigger or 'expands' as it cools below 4° C.

Imagine a bit of water, in the shape of a cube.

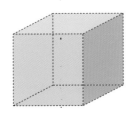

If the water is cooled, it turns to ice and gets bigger or 'expands' as it freezes.

However its weight is still the same because there is the same amount of water.

This means ice is less 'dense' than liquid water and so it floats.

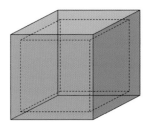

This is a piece of copper tube, the same metal that Fiery Fox's boiler is made from.

It has two end plugs. One has a threaded hole so the tube can be filled up with water and sealed with a bolt.

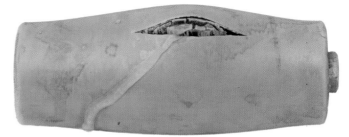

The tube was filled with water, sealed up with the bolt and put in the freezer overnight. (The bolt is visible at the right hand end.)

The water inside has frozen and expanded with such force that it has burst the metal tube open. You can see the ice inside.

This is exactly what would happen to Fiery Fox's boiler if it was left full of water over the winter and froze!

Funny Question

Why do grapes go up and down in a glass of fizzy drink?

If you watch very closely you can work out why.

Answers by email to
info@petersrailway.com

If ice was more dense than water, the Titanic would not have been lost.

Fairy Hillocks

Back indoors and enjoying a cup of tea, Grandpa asked, "Did I ever tell you the story about the Fairy Hillocks in the winter of 1895?"

"No," said Peter, "but I'm not too sure I like stories about fairies."

"It's not what you think," said Grandpa, settling down into his armchair.

"The Highland Railway, north of Inverness," he began, "is a very remote and desolate place. There are hardly any houses or roads and, apart from the railway, there are miles and miles where there is simply no sign of human existence."

"One part of the line goes through a landscape which is dotted about with little mounds. The engine drivers thought they looked like fairy hillocks, so that's what they called the area."

 "Well, in the winter of 1895," he went on, "there was a series of terrible snow storms and the line was often blocked. The snow had brought down all the telephone wires and there weren't any mobile phones in those days. Several trains were completely buried under metres of snow, and sometimes for days on end."

"Whatever happened to the passengers?" asked Peter.

"Ah, luckily for them," replied Grandpa, "they were usually rescued after a day or two. But it wasn't easy; the rescuers would have to walk through the snow to get to them."

"One of the first trains to be lost in the storms was a fish special, full of fish caught at Wick and on its way to market. It had been heading South through a fierce blizzard and finally got stuck at Fairy Hillocks. The crew realised it was hopeless, so they hastily abandoned the train and walked away before the snow got too deep. It was stuck there for ten whole days, completely buried."

"Pooh!" said Peter, wrinkling up his nose. "That fish must have smelt awful by the time they got back to it."

"Well that was the funny thing," laughed Grandpa. "The snow had worked like a giant freezer and the fish was still in perfect condition. So they dug the train out and delivered the fish, as if nothing had happened!"

"I wonder if the railway ever told the fish market?" he smiled.

Grandpa had read this story in a book about the history of the Highland Railway and he went to get it. Then he showed them one of the photographs which had been taken of the snow in 1895, the same year as his story.

"That is a snow plough, charging the drifts at Fairy Hillocks," said Grandpa, pointing at the picture.

"I can't see a plough," said Peter, before he had looked at it properly. "Just a lot of snow."

"That's the beauty of the photograph," said Grandpa. "The plough was being pushed by three locomotives but you can't see it or even the engines. There's just a great blur of flying snow. In fact the only way you can tell there is a steam engine there at all, is because some of the snow is rather black. It's the smoke from the leading locomotive's chimney!"

"I enjoyed that story," said Grandma, "and I'm glad you managed to clear the snow drifts today." Then, putting on her spectacles, she picked up her newspaper to do the crossword.

Three engines and a snow plough charging a drift at Fairy Hillocks in Caithness - Scotland in 1895.
Taken by A Johnston - Wick.

"That's odd," she said. "I can't read a thing."

"Perhaps your glasses are dirty," said Peter helpfully, but with a cheeky grin on his face.

Grandma took off her glasses and tried to clean them. But her finger poked right through the frame where the lenses should have been.

Peter collapsed in giggles and Grandma realised he had played a trick on her.

"What *have* you done?" she asked.

"I undid the little screws which hold the lenses into the frame, with a tiny watchmaker's screwdriver from the workshop," answered Peter.

"Here they are," he said still shaking with giggles. And he handed the lenses back to Grandma.

"How am I supposed to put them back together when I can't see properly?" she asked. "You do it, you cheeky monkey."

With her glasses repaired and back on her nose, she looked over the top of them and said, "Just remember Peter, Grannies can play practical jokes on their grandsons too. Just you watch out……"

SNOW PLOUGH AT WORK

Snow Plough at Work.

This old photograph from 1895 shows how the snow plough lifts the snow and throws it clear to the sides.
You can see the smoke from the engine.

Taken by A Johnston - Wick.

Courtesy Wick Heritage Museum

Station Lights

One of the problems with operating the railway in winter is that it gets dark early in the evenings. They didn't want anyone, especially Grandma, to trip or fall at the stations. That would never do.

It was Peter's dad Colin, who came up with the solution. "I'll make you some electric lights to put on the platforms," he said one evening. "I'll make them to look like miniature old fashioned street lamps."

"Good idea," said Grandpa. "Could you make them run on 12 volts? It will be safe like that and we can run them from old tractor batteries."

"We could have a battery for each station and when they go flat we can just put them on the train and bring them up to the farm for recharging."

Colin was as good as his word and a few weeks later the lamps were finished. They were made from garden lanterns but he had replaced the candle holders with 12 volt bulbs. The posts to hold them were old bits of metal pipe and the wires to supply the electricity were hidden in the posts.

Over the next few afternoons Peter, Grandpa and Colin installed the lamps at the stations. They set the posts in holes in the ground and then connected them all together with some electric cable. The last job was to wire up a switch and connect the lamps to a battery.

As it got darker, they went to raise steam so they could take Grandma to inspect the works. They also lit the stove in her Saloon Carriage as it was a cold night.

When everything was ready, Grandma came out and got into the 'Granny Wagon' as she now knew it was called. Warm and comfortable inside, it was a really luxurious way to travel.

The scene at Gerald's Cross station was splendid. The lights were twinkling in the night and steam was drifting from Fiery Fox as they set off down the line. Peter was driving, Grandpa was on the guard's van at the back and Grandma was travelling First Class.

Once away from the station it was pitch black so Peter drove slowly. He tooted the whistle from time to time, to let animals know they were coming.

Then in the distance, looming out of the night, he could see the lights of Yewston station, in the garden at Woodland Cottage. At least he could now judge when to put the brakes on.

It looked great and Peter's mum Jo had got cups of tea ready, to drink at the station. It was quite a party by electric light.

Of course, they all had to go for a few runs round the whole line. Even Kitty and Harry had been allowed to stay up late to ride in the train and see the lights. Kitty went to put some coal in the firebox and then they both rode with Grandma in her cosy warm saloon.

They were doing the last run and taking everyone home when it started to rain. The rails had become wet and shiny. Now when they approached the stations, the lamps on the platform were reflected up the lines in little ribbons of light coming towards them. It looked magical.

While Kitty and Harry were going to bed, Peter, Grandpa and Colin were sitting in the shelter at the station with Fiery Fox simmering outside. After a while the talk turned to their plan to build a waterwheel on the river.

The idea was to put it at the waterfall and use the river to generate electricity to power the house and farm.

"It's an excellent idea," said Colin, "especially with the price of electricity going up and up. If you and Peter are going to build it as your summer project, I would love to help you."

"The only question is," he added, "will you need to get permission to use the river?"

"I think you're right," agreed Grandpa. "It would be much better to ask before we start construction. I'll write to the Rivers Authority, first thing in the morning."

It was getting late and when Peter and Colin went indoors, Grandpa drove the train back up to the farm, taking Grandma home with him.

He put the engine and train back in the shed, let the fire out and turned in for the night.

What is Electricity?

Electricity is made of tiny charged particles called Electrons. They are so tiny that 100 million of them would fit in the width of one atom. And an atom itself is incredibly small; a human hair is about 1 million atoms wide.

For electricity to do something useful, a lot of electrons need to flow round a 'circuit'. This flow of electrons is called an electric current. (Sometimes the charged particles which move in a circuit are called 'ions' but we won't worry about that just now.)

Conductors and Insulators

Electric currents usually flow down metal wires or cables. The metal normally used is copper because it is a good 'conductor' of electricity.

Current is measured in 'amperes' or 'amps' for short.

Electricity will not flow through materials called 'insulators'. Examples of insulators are air, glass, plastic and brick.

Electrons in a copper wire
Copper wire contains lots of electrons, a bit like a hose pipe full of water. The electrons are not held rigidly in position but can drift about.

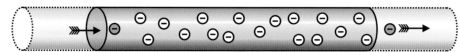

If you push an electron in one end, then one pops out of the other end.

Copper cable with two wires
The insulation stops the wires touching and making a 'short circuit'.

Simple circuit

A battery is connected to a light bulb with copper wires.

The battery is like an electron pump and pushes electrons round the circuit. It pushes electrons out of its 'negative' or − terminal and takes them back into its 'positive' or + terminal.

(Note: The little black arrows in the wire in this diagram show the direction of the electrons. However electrical engineers are a funny lot and always show current going the other way; from positive to negative. The current direction is shown with red arrows.)

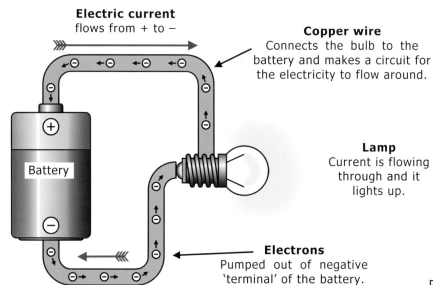

Electric current
flows from + to −

Copper wire
Connects the bulb to the battery and makes a circuit for the electricity to flow around.

Lamp
Current is flowing through and it lights up.

Battery

Electrons
Pumped out of negative 'terminal' of the battery.

The Switch

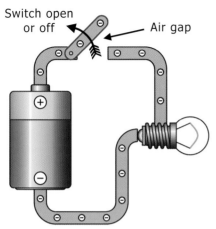

Switch open or off — Air gap

Electrons cannot get across the air gap so no current flows

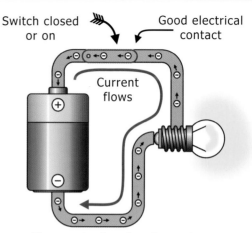

Switch closed or on — Good electrical contact

Current flows

The gap is closed and completes the circuit. Current can flow.

Switch or Circuit Breaker

A simple switch has now been included in the circuit. In the left hand drawing it is open or off and the lamp is not lit. In the right hand picture it is closed or on and the lamp is lit.

Another name for a switch is 'circuit breaker'. This describes what it does perfectly - it breaks the circuit.

When the switch is open or off, there is a gap in the circuit. Air is a good electrical insulator, so the current cannot flow and the lamp goes out.

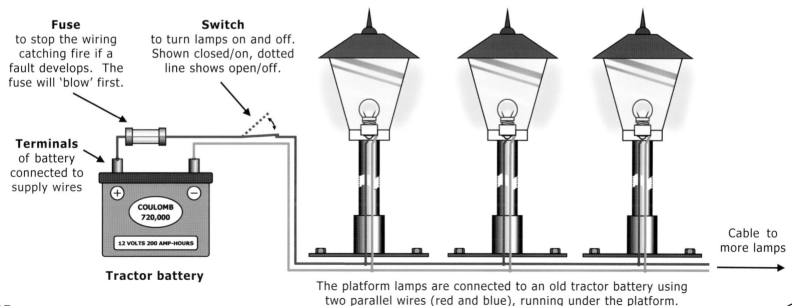

Fuse
to stop the wiring catching fire if a fault develops. The fuse will 'blow' first.

Switch
to turn lamps on and off. Shown closed/on, dotted line shows open/off.

Terminals
of battery connected to supply wires

COULOMB
720,000

12 VOLTS 200 AMP-HOURS

Tractor battery

Cable to more lamps

The platform lamps are connected to an old tractor battery using two parallel wires (red and blue), running under the platform.

The Watermill

One morning while Peter was eating his breakfast at Woodland Cottage, he heard a loud whistling outside.

He rushed out, just in time to see Grandpa arriving on Fiery Fox. He was grinning from ear to ear.

"I've got a letter from the Rivers Authority," he shouted when he had stopped the train. "It's good news: We've got permission to build the watermill."

Peter too was excited. It was the beginning of the summer holidays and now they had a really good project on their hands. There was not even the tiniest chance of getting bored.

Grandpa started to explain what they would have to do:

"We'll make a waterwheel with buckets or scoops all round the outside. Then we can guide some water, from the top of the waterfall, down a chute and onto the wheel. As the buckets on one side of the wheel fill up, the weight of the water will push it round and turn an electric generator."

"We will have to construct a small building to house the generator," he continued, "and we'll make one of the walls very strong, so it can support the wheel."

"It sounds great," said Peter, who couldn't wait to get going. "Can we make a start on it today?"

"Jump on the train then," said Grandpa. "We will go up to the farm and get some tools. Then we'll drive back to the waterfall and measure its height. We will also work out the best place to put the mill building."

Back at the farm, they loaded some tools and measuring tapes into the engineers' wagon and steamed back down the line to the waterfall.

"The first thing to measure is how far the water drops over the falls," explained Grandpa. "It will tell us what size to make the wheel."

They stood on the river bank and got themselves level with the water at the top of the falls. Then they dangled the tape measure down until it just touched the water at the bottom.

"Three metres," called out Grandpa. "That's higher than I thought it would be. But it's good because the higher the drop, the more power we'll be able to generate."

Next they looked at the river bank to see where they could build the mill. There was a perfect spot, just below the falls. It would need a bit of digging out, but nothing too serious.

"I think we'll go back up to the farm now," said Grandpa, when they had drawn a sketch of the site. "We can have a hunt around and see what we can find to make the waterwheel from."

It didn't take them long before they found what they needed. The old tractor which had provided the bearing for the railway turntable was still there and its back wheels would make an excellent centre part for the waterwheel.

"And look," pointed Peter. "The other half of the back axle will make a perfect bearing. The wheel will just bolt onto the hub, like it does now."

"Excellent," agreed Grandpa. "Now all we need to find is something we can make the buckets from."

Just beside the old tractor was a stack of old oil drums. They had originally contained lubricating oil, but had been empty for years. Grandpa had kept them, thinking they would be useful one day.

"If we were to cut them in two, lengthways," he showed Peter, "each drum would make two of the buckets. We would just have to weld them round the outside of the wheels. With a bit of extra strengthening, they will do the job perfectly."

Back indoors, Grandpa did a few calculations on the flow of water and how much power they could generate.

The drums were about 85 cm long so they would make a water chute the same width, to guide the water onto the wheel. He calculated that about 200 litres of water could flow down it every second.

"That's about a bath-full of water," he told Peter. "Can you imagine how much hard work it would be to lift a full bath up to a height of 3 metres, every second? Well that's the amount of power which we will be getting from the water falling down."

He did a few more calculations to work it out a bit more scientifically.

"Six kilowatts of power," he declared. "But that's the absolute maximum we could get from the water. There will be losses in the generator and some of the water will spill over the buckets. So I think we should aim for four kilowatts of electricity. Then we won't be disappointed."

It was still a lot. Four kilowatts is four *thousand* watts of power and a modern light bulb only takes around 20 watts. They would be able to power 200 lights!

"What else are we going to need?" wondered Peter. "I'll write down a list."

They would have to build the water chute and also make some sort of sluice or gate valve at one end, so they could control the flow of water.

The electric generator was a bit of a problem until Grandpa remembered he had a large electric motor which used to power a grain drying fan.

"We can use the motor in reverse to work as a generator," he explained. "If you spin most types of motor, they will generate electricity instead of using it. The old drier motor will save us a lot of money."

The pulleys and belts to take the drive from the wheel to the generator could all come from an old combine harvester. It hadn't worked for years but, like the tractor, a lot of the parts were still in perfect working order.

"I've still got plenty of old bricks and cement to build the mill house," Grandpa remembered. "But we'll have to go on a bit of a hunt for enough timber to make the roof."

Next on the list was the electric cable to connect the generator to the house and farm. They had paced out the distance on the way back from the river; it was just over 900 metres and would have to carry 4 kilowatts.

"The cable is going to be rather expensive, if we buy it new," said Grandpa, thoughtfully scratching his head. "I think I'll give the local scrap yard a call later and see if they can come up with something. It still won't be cheap though, because even scrap copper is valuable."

The last item which he could think of was an electric control box.

"The generator is going to need a controller to keep the voltage constant when we turn lights on and off," he explained. "Otherwise they will be either too dim or go pop!"

"I can't imagine we'll be able to make one," he said sadly, "so I'll just have to bite the bullet and buy one."

It only took a few calls to track down what he was looking for. The company he found was very helpful and said they would send one out straight away as it was a standard product.

The next day they went on a giant treasure hunt round the farm, collecting together all the stuff they would need. They stacked it up near the railway, ready for transporting to the building site.

They rolled the two old tractor wheels up to the workshop. The really difficult job was removing the old tyres which had perished and gone hard.

Then back down to the old tractor to remove the second half of the back axle. Just like the other side, which they had used for the turntable, it was in good condition. The hub would bolt onto the centre of the waterwheel and the bearing would allow it to turn freely. The drive shaft would stick in through the wall of the mill, to drive the generator inside.

Back at the workshop, they clamped the wheels together and welded them up to make a really solid centre. Even better, it was just the right width for the oil drum buckets.

Next up to the workshop went the drums. With the angle grinder, they cut five of them lengthways along the middle and stacked the ten buckets outside.

It didn't take long to clamp each one to the side of the wheel and weld them into position. The waterwheel was beginning to take shape.

"It looks good," said Grandpa. "But I don't think it's strong enough yet. We'll have to weld on some extra bits of metal to stiffen the whole thing up. Don't forget, the water will be trying to pull it to bits all the time it is running."

The next day, with the welding done, they brushed on a coat of paint and finally stood back to admire their handiwork. It looked great.

While they were chatting together, who should come up the road in his battered old lorry, but the scrap man.

"Perfect timing," Grandpa called out to him. "Have you got some cable for us?"

"Will this do you Guvnor?" he replied as he unloaded a huge reel. "It's really heavy duty stuff. But it's all I could get."

"That's fine," agreed Grandpa. "It's better too thick than too thin. I would hate it to get hot and catch fire!"

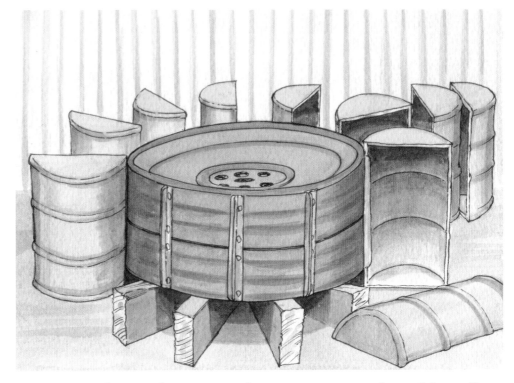

They haggled a bit over the price and Grandpa counted out some notes from his wallet.

"It's no good giving scrap men a cheque," he told Peter later. "They only understand cash."

With the cable delivered, they had everything they needed. Watermill construction could now begin.

The Watermill

A waterwheel extracts energy from falling water. The turning wheel can be used to do something useful like generating electricity. This wheel is of the 'overshot' type because the water drops onto it from above. The other type of waterwheel is called 'undershot' where the water passes under the wheel, turning it as it goes.

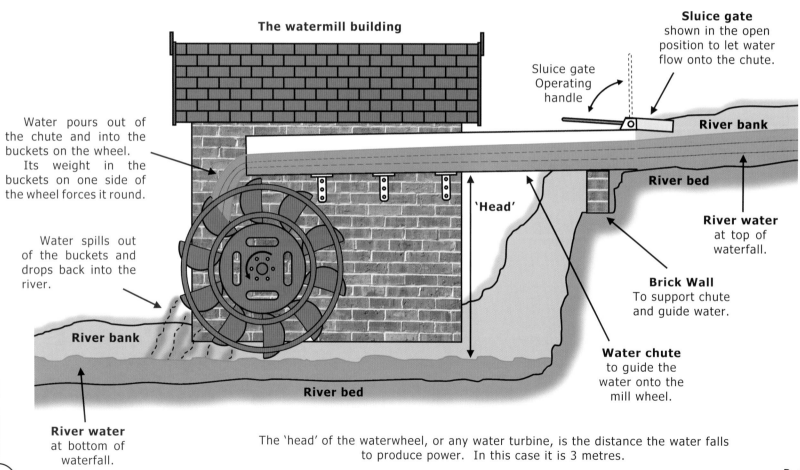

The watermill building

Sluice gate
shown in the open position to let water flow onto the chute.

Sluice gate Operating handle

River bank

River bed

Water pours out of the chute and into the buckets on the wheel.
Its weight in the buckets on one side of the wheel forces it round.

'Head'

River water
at top of waterfall.

Brick Wall
To support chute and guide water.

Water spills out of the buckets and drops back into the river.

River bank

Water chute
to guide the water onto the mill wheel.

River bed

River water
at bottom of waterfall.

The 'head' of the waterwheel, or any water turbine, is the distance the water falls to produce power. In this case it is 3 metres.

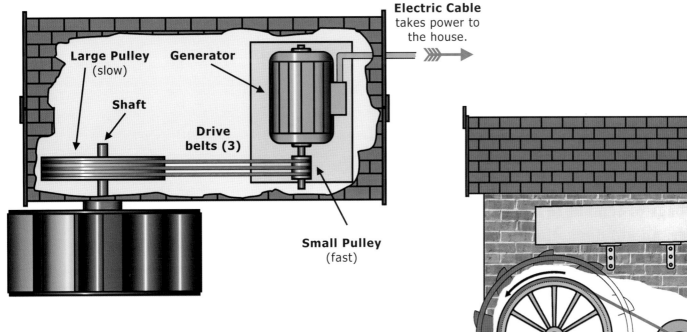

Electric Cable
takes power to
the house.

Large Pulley
(slow)

Generator

Shaft

**Drive
belts (3)**

Small Pulley
(fast)

Watermill Plan - View from above

The roof has been cut away to show the generator (blue) and pulleys and drive belts inside.

The drive from the waterwheel is brought in by the shaft (purple) which turns the large pulley (green).

Three drive belts (red) transfer the power from the large pulley to the small pulley on the generator.

The bearing (red) from the old tractor can be seen between the waterwheel and the wall.

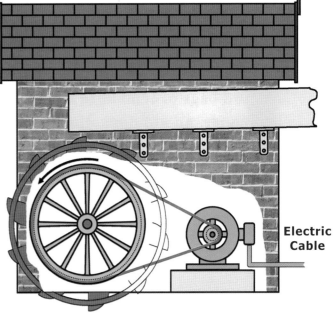

**Electric
Cable**

Watermill - Side View

In this view, the wall and wheel have been cut away to show the machinery from the side.

The waterwheel turns quite slowly but the generator needs to be turned much faster to generate electricity.

A large pulley turned by the waterwheel drives a much smaller pulley on the generator so that the speed of rotation is increased.

Construction Begins

The next morning they lit up Fiery Fox and made all the usual preparations. Peter took particular care with the oiling today as she was going to work very hard. There was an awful lot of heavy material to take down to the building site at the waterfall.

They steamed up and down the track for most of the day. There were bricks, concrete blocks and bags of cement to deliver. Then there was the generator, pulleys, belts, nuts and bolts, timber, an old door, the cement mixer, bags of sand.... The list went on and on.

By the time they were done, Fiery Fox had hauled twenty one freight trains and it was getting dark.

The following day they set to work on the foundations. Grandpa's old digger made light work of digging out the trenches. It was a demonstration of the power of hydraulics.

As they dug out the soil, Grandpa dropped it into the river at the top of the waterfall to make a dam at one side. It would stop the water flowing where they wanted to build the mill house. After all, building walls in a river would be a bit difficult! All the river water could still flow over the far side of the falls.

It was hot and hard work, mixing up the concrete to pour into the trenches and to make the solid floor. But, by the end of the week the foundations were finished. Grandpa had been cunning and had set some bolts into the concrete floor while it was still wet. They were in just the right position to bolt down the generator.

The next couple of weeks passed with building the walls and putting up the roof. They made the wall next to the river extra strong as it was going to have to hold the bearing and the weight of the wheel.

It was pleasant working in the warm weather and Minnie and Cato thought it was great too. No work for them though; they just lay basking in the sun and dozing the day away, or watching Peter and Grandpa.

Once the mill building was finished, they could start putting the machinery together.

The first operation was to bolt the bearing to its wall, with long bolts which went right through the bricks.

They had left a hole especially for the drive shaft to go through, to the inside.

Then, using the digger as a crane, they carried the waterwheel down to the mill and lowered it into position. Peter jiggled it onto the hub, put the nuts on and tightened them up with a large spanner. The wheel was on, but would it turn freely on its bearing?

Just then Cato, who had shown a great interest in all the goings-on, decided to inspect the waterwheel. He jumped from his wall, into one of the buckets.

He wasn't very heavy, but his weight started to turn the wheel and he slowly descended until it tipped him out into the river!

Poor Cato leapt out and shook himself dry and sat with his back to them for the rest of the day. It didn't help his feelings that Peter and Grandpa couldn't stop laughing.

"Oh well, at least we know the bearing works," said Peter, when he could speak again. "Thanks Cato, that was really helpful of you."

With the wheel installed, they turned their attention to making the chute to run the water onto it. It only needed to be a simple channel or U shape with a hinged sluice gate at one end, a bit like a large cat-flap.

A few days work, cutting up some sheets of metal and welding them together soon had it finished. Then a long handle was welded onto the hinged gate so they could open and close it easily. Last, Grandpa drilled some holes for a metal pin which would hold it open in different positions. The next day they used the digger to carry it down to the mill.

At the building site, they carefully lowered the chute into position. One end rested on a small wall just under the dry waterfall. The other end was bolted to the side of the mill, a little above the wheel. They spent the rest of the day finishing the support wall with more bricks and cement, so the water would be guided into the chute.

After leaving the cement to dry for a couple of days, it was time for the first test. They started up the digger and dug out the dam. The water washed past, up to the closed sluice gate.

"I can't wait to see it running!" said Peter excitedly.

"We had better give it a trial run," said Grandpa, who could hardly wait himself. "Could you let a little water through?"

Peter pulled the lever to crack open the sluice for a moment. A trickle of water ran down the chute, onto the wheel and it started to turn. Things were looking good, but there was more to do.

Over the next few days they finished off the mill by installing the generator, pulleys and belts. At last it was time for another test and Peter went outside to open the sluice again.

Inside the mill, the large pulley started to turn slowly, spinning the small pulley on the generator much faster. The drive belts were transmitting the power from one to the other. The two engineers, young and old, stood watching the wheels go round for ages. It was mesmerising and they were simply enjoying the sight of all their hard work taking shape at last.

"Well, Peter," said Grandpa, "that's the mill finished, except of course, for connecting it to the house. And we can make a start on that tomorrow......"

Peter went outside to shut the sluice gate, the machinery fell silent and they went back up to the farm for a well earned meal.

Energy and Power

There are lots of different types of energy and they are often converted from one type to another by machines.

Mechanical energy, when a force pushes something through a distance. (sometimes called 'work'.)

Heat energy, such as a boiler full of hot water and steam.

Chemical energy. Coal, petrol and diesel contain a lot of chemical energy which can be converted into heat energy by burning.

Electrical energy can be used to light lamps, turn electric motors or operate computers.

Motion or Kinetic energy. Anything moving contains kinetic energy. The brakes of a car or train use friction to convert the kinetic energy to heat. That is why the brakes get hot when slowing down a train, car or bicycle.

Potential energy could be the energy of something which has been lifted up against gravity. For example a bicycle at the top of a hill has potential energy. This can be converted into motion or kinetic energy by freewheeling down the hill.

The river water at the top of the waterfall contains a lot of **potential energy**. It has a potential or ability to do work as it falls down.

The water loses some of its **potential energy** as it drops. The whole point of the waterwheel is to extract that potential energy and convert it into **mechanical energy** or '**work**'.

The water at the bottom has less potential energy than it did at the top.

Generator converts the **mechanical energy** or '**work**' done by the wheel into **electrical energy**.

Electrical energy Transmitted to the house in a cable.

Power

While energy is measured in joules, power is measured in watts. Power is the rate at which work is done or energy is converted from one form to another. The faster the work is done, (or energy converted) the greater the power.

For example a 2000 watt electric kettle would boil the water twice as fast as a 1000 watt kettle. (1000 watts is called a kilowatt.)

The Law of Conservation of Energy

This is one of the most important laws in the whole of science. It doesn't matter how energy is converted into whatever form, but it is always 'conserved'. It is never lost.

The total amount of energy in the whole universe is always the same!

The Steam Locomotive - an Energy Converter

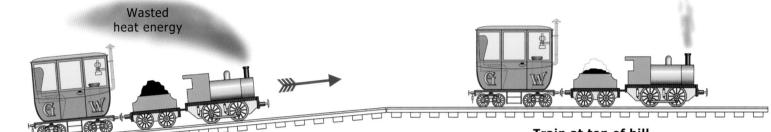

Wasted heat energy

Engine lifting heavy train up a gradient

The energy to lift the heavy train up the hill, against gravity, is in the tender of the engine. It is chemical energy in the coal.

The chemical energy in the coal is being converted into heat energy by burning it in the firebox and this heat is given to the water to make it into steam. The steam contains heat and pressure energy.

The energy in the steam is converted by the pistons and cylinders into mechanical energy or work, to lift the train up the hill.

Train at top of hill

At the top of the hill, the train has gained potential energy. This was obtained from the chemical energy in the coal. You can see that some of the coal in the tender has been used up.

Unfortunately not all of the chemical energy in the coal has been converted into work and potential energy. Most of it was lost up the chimney as waste heat. In fact, less than 5% of the energy in the coal will have done something useful, the rest (95%) is wasted.

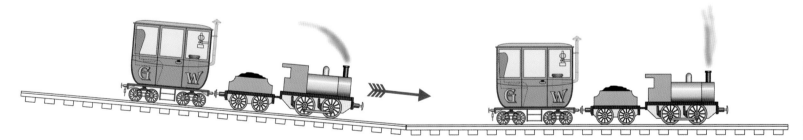

Train coasting downhill

Now the train is coasting downhill. The driver has put on the engine's brakes, to stop the train going too fast. The energy to make the train move is coming from the potential energy which it had at the top of the hill.

The potential energy is being converted by friction into heat in the brakes. They are shown here red hot and this could really happen on a heavy freight train coming down a long gradient using the engine's brakes to control the speed. On the very early engines, the brake blocks were made of wood and they would often catch fire.

Train finally stopped

After descending the hill, the brakes were left on for a bit longer to stop the train.

The motion or 'kinetic' energy has been turned into heat by the brakes, using friction.

Sadly it is true that in almost all machines and processes, all the expensive energy at the beginning (electricity, coal, petrol etc.) finally ends up as waste heat.

The Duke's Dog

Grandpa asked after dinner, "Have I ever told you the story of Driver Shelvey's Dog?"

Grandma and Peter had never heard of Driver Shelvey, let alone his dog, so Grandpa started his story:

"A very long time ago, in 1865, a small dog was walking around the streets of London. He was tired, cold, hungry and miserable because he had no home to go to and he was lost."

"For no particular reason he walked in through the entrance of Euston station. The place was packed with people, all going in different directions. They were so busy with their own affairs that none of them even noticed the sad little dog, let alone stopped to comfort him."

He was beginning to give up hope of ever finding a home to live in, or someone to love and take care of him."

"He walked along one of the platforms, dodging between peoples' legs until he ended up standing next to a locomotive. There he stopped for a while, enjoying the warmth which radiated out from its fire and boiler."

"All of a sudden a huge man, who was standing next to him, bent down and patted him on the head and said 'Are you cold, little feller? Would you like to come up on the footplate of my engine, to warm up for a while?'"

"The dog didn't understand the words of course, but he did know a kind voice when he heard one. He gave a little bark of thanks and jumped up on the footplate, wagging his tail wildly."

"The driver's name was Mr Shelvey, although all the other drivers called him 'The Duke'. They'd given him this grand nickname because he had an enormous nose, just like the Duke of Wellington, the famous General and Prime Minister of the day."

"It was quite clear to the Duke," continued Grandpa, "that the little dog was very pleased to be with him on the locomotive. So when it was time to go, he put him in a safe place on the tender to enjoy a ride."

"Once the Duke and his fireman had got the heavy train under way and accelerating towards the North, he turned to the dog and said 'If you are going to keep us company on our journeys, I'd better give you a name. How about Snatchburry?'"

"The two of them became real friends and after that, Snatchburry went with the Duke on all of his trips, riding on the tender."

"Sometimes he'd curl up at the back of the tender for a sleep. He couldn't fall off because there was a raised edge all round. But his favourite position was standing on top of the tool box where he had a good view of the line ahead."

"He'd stand there for mile after mile. With the wind flapping his ears about and blowing the shaggy hair back from his small pretty face."

"What a charming story," said Grandma.

"What a lucky dog," added Peter.

"Once," continued Grandpa, who hadn't finished his story, "Snatchburry was a bit late and missed the train. He wasn't a bit concerned though. He knew exactly which direction his master had gone and just jumped on another engine, which was going that way."

"When he got to the last station on the line, he hopped off and trotted over to the yard. There he found the Duke, oiling up his locomotive, ready for the return run."

"How clever," said Peter. "Whoever would have thought a dog could work all that out by itself."

"That wasn't all," smiled Grandpa. "Over the years he even learnt to read the signals and would always give a warning bark when he saw a red light."

"I don't know how he did it, but he always knew his engine, even though there were lots in the shed, all exactly the same."

Grandma and Peter both thought it was a lovely story. One of Grandpa's best.

"I shall fall asleep tonight, thinking about Snatchburry, with his ears flying in the wind, riding the express," said Grandma. "It's a much better story for falling asleep to than your one about terrified passengers, locked in carriages, hurtling backwards into the night!" she laughed.

"One day I'll tell you the story about 'Ocky' the cat," said Grandpa. "You'll like that one too. But not tonight, it's too late."

Wired Up

The great Crossacres Hydro-Electric Power Station was well underway, but there was still the job of connecting the generator to the house and farm.

Grandpa explained to Peter that they would have to run the electric cable, between the mill and the house. Then they would connect one end of the cable to the generator and the other end to the new control box.

Mr Sparks, the local electrician, had already installed the control box on a wall in the corner of the kitchen. (Mr Sparks isn't his real name of course. But almost all electricians seem to be called Sparks, because of what happens if they make a mistake!)

Grandpa and Peter took a careful look at it: A square metal box, it had a large meter on the front, labelled 'Hydro Volts'. There was also a lever on the side with three positions: 'Mains Power', 'Off' and 'Hydro Power'.

Grandpa explained that when the house is running on mains electricity, like everyone else's, the switch will be set to 'Mains Power'. But as long as there is enough water in the river, the switch will be kept on 'Hydro Power'. The house will be disconnected from the mains supply cable and powered by the cable from the mill.

Peter wanted to know about the large meter on the front.

"It shows the voltage from the generator," explained Grandpa. "In Britain, mains electricity is at 240 volts and the control box will always try to keep the electricity from the mill exactly the same. It will only drop below 240 volts if we draw too much power and the generator can't cope. And then what happens Peter?" he asked.

"You'll just have to turn a few lights off," the young engineer laughed.

"You've got it in one," said Grandpa. "But there is one important thing I must tell you about electricity: It is extremely dangerous at high voltages like this and can easily kill you. We will have to be very careful."

They decided to bury the cable in a trench in the ground as it would be completely safe and out of harm's way.

It was a major job, but a lot of fun. They got the digger going again, (with the usual cloud of black smoke as its old diesel engine fired up) and rolled the reel of cable into the wide loading shovel. A piece of pipe through the centre of the reel let it turn quite easily.

They would dig a bit of trench then drive the digger along, unrolling the cable behind them. Then dig the next bit and so on, until they got to the mill. Finally, back along the trench, pushing the earth back in, to cover up the cable.

It was hard work and took them a long time to do, but then getting electricity from any power station to where it is needed is a major undertaking.

Connecting the cable at each end was not a complicated job, but Grandpa wasn't taking any chances.

"There will be a lot of power going through the connections," he explained. "It's at high voltage and simply too dangerous for us to do on our own. I've asked Mr Sparks to come out this afternoon, to connect up both ends and make sure it's all safe."

Mr Sparks didn't take long. Down at the mill, he stripped the insulation off the cable. Then he bolted the bare copper wires to the terminals on the side of the generator and replaced the cover plate.

Up at the house, it wasn't so different. They had already pushed the cable in through a ventilation hole and run it up the wall to the control box. After stripping off the insulation, Mr Sparks pulled the switch to the 'Off' position, cutting the power to the house. Then he opened up the box, put the wires into the terminals and tightened up the screws.

"The job's a good'un," he said confidently, as he closed the box.

"Why don't you turn the mains back on Peter?" he suggested. "You'll be amazed at how heavy the switch is."

Peter took hold of the big lever and was ready to push it back up, to turn on the mains. He was rather nervous as he knew there was a lot of power behind the switch.

Now at this moment, and unseen by Peter, Grandma had crept up behind him. She was holding a balloon and a pin....

Holding his breath, Peter pushed the lever up. There was a loud clank from inside the box and the lights flashed on. But that was nothing compared to the huge bang from Grandma popping the balloon, just behind him.

Poor Peter! He jumped about a foot off the floor.

He spun round and saw Grandma, holding the remains of the balloon and roaring with laughter.

"I.. I.. thought the control box had b..blown up," he stammered.

"Well that'll teach you to play practical jokes on your Granny!" she giggled.

It took him a few minutes to recover and see the funny side, but at least they were quits now. Until he played another joke on Grandma that is........

Unfortunately it was getting a bit too late to test the generator that day.

"Don't worry," said Grandpa. "We've got all of tomorrow, so there's no point in rushing it. It'll give you something to look forward to."

"And besides," he added laughing, "I don't think your nerves could stand working that switch again tonight!"

The Electric Motor and Generator

Electric motors come in all shapes and sizes, but they all do the same thing: They use electricity to make a shaft rotate.
Electric generators are the reverse of a motor: If their shaft is rotated fast enough they generate electricity.
Many types of motor will work in reverse, as a generator: If you spin the motor's shaft, it will make electricity.

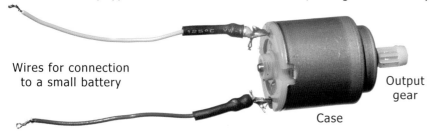

Wires for connection
to a small battery

Output
gear

Case

Electric motor from a toy car.

This small electric motor operates from a battery, which is connected to the two wires.

The output shaft with the gear spins very fast and drives the car through reduction gears to reduce the speed.

Motor as a Generator

Here the motor has been connected to 3 tiny lamps. They are called LEDs or Light Emitting Diodes. (LEDs are useful because they don't use much electricity.)

The motor is being spun round with fingers and the LEDs light up. The motor is working as a generator and making enough electricity to work the lamps.

You can try this experiment yourself. You only need an old battery powered toy or model which can be taken to pieces for the motor. LEDs are often found in toys and torches. (Note: You will probably find that the motor will only light the LED if it is spun in one direction.)

Electromagnetism

Motors and generators all work using the principle of 'electromagnetism'. A wire with an electric current flowing in it, near a magnet will try to move sideways. (As long as it is lined up the right way.) The opposite is true too: If you move a loop of wire across a magnetic field (across the end of a magnet), then a current will flow in the wire. All the clever bits inside a motor or generator are simply to move a coil of wire through a magnetic field and connect it to the outside.

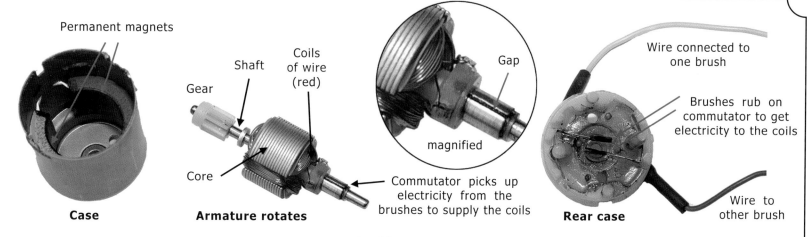

Permanent magnets

Gear

Shaft

Coils of wire (red)

Core

Case

Armature rotates

Commutator picks up electricity from the brushes to supply the coils

Gap

magnified

Wire connected to one brush

Brushes rub on commutator to get electricity to the coils

Wire to other brush

Rear case

Inside a motor

The red coils form 'electro-magnets' which are attracted to and then repelled from the permanent magnets in sequence, causing the armature to turn. It is the action of the brushes on the commutator, as it turns, which switches the direction of the current in the coils. The changing direction of current causes the coils to be attracted to or repelled from the permanent magnets in the case. (note the little insulating gap between segments of the commutator.)

The V-Belt Drive

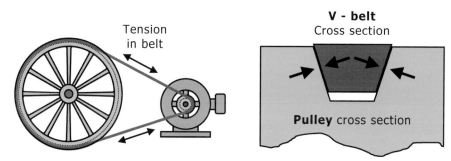

Tension in belt

V - belt
Cross section

Pulley cross section

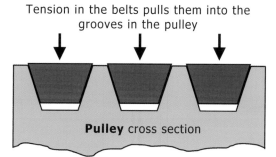

Tension in the belts pulls them into the grooves in the pulley

Pulley cross section

The V - belt runs in a groove round a pulley. Both the sides of the groove and the belt are tapered or 'wedge' shaped.

A small amount of tension in the belt pulls it into the groove and the wedge action makes a large gripping force on its sides. All the drive is on the sides of the belt and not the bottom, where there is a gap.

3 belts are used on the waterwheel drive, to spread the load.

If one of the belts breaks, the lights won't go out in the house as the other two are strong enough to take the load.

Throw the Switch

Early the next morning, Peter and Grandpa lit the fire in Fiery Fox, coupled on the train and set off to the mill. The river was flowing fast and there was plenty of water going over the falls.

"That water will soon be going through the mill and generating electricity," said Grandpa smiling. "Just think how much energy has been wasted over the years, when it could have been doing something useful."

With that thought, they both grabbed the lever on the sluice gate and pushed it open.

Water rushed down the chute in a raging torrent. Pouring into the drums on one side of the wheel, it started to turn.

"We had better check the machinery," said Peter, "before we go away and leave it running." Inside, everything was turning and humming quietly; the pulleys and belts transferring the power from the wheel to the generator. They made regular checks of the temperature of the bearings and the tension in the belts.

"That's Ok," said Grandpa, after an hour. "Everything's fine. Let's go on down to Woodland Cottage and collect the rest of the family. They wouldn't want to miss the switching on ceremony."

With the family up at the farm, Peter and Grandpa were ready for the switchover from mains electricity to the generator at the mill. There were a few lights on in the house, but they had turned most electrical things off for the initial test.

Everyone was gathered round. The voltmeter on the control box was showing 240 volts from the generator. So far, so good....

Grandpa pulled the switch from the mains position to off. The lights went out and Grandma's radio in the kitchen fell silent.

They swapped places and Peter now held the lever. It was the moment they had been looking forward to. Would it work?

"Throw the switch!" shouted Grandpa.

Peter pulled down hard and, with a loud clank, the lights came back on and the radio started chattering again.

The voltmeter was steady at 240v. The house was running on hydro power.

"That's just magic...." cried Grandma, "or perhaps I should say it's more like clever engineering by you two. We won't ever have to pay another electric bill."

Grandpa explained that if they used too much electricity, it would overload the generator. The voltage would start to drop and they would have to turn things off.

"You'll know soon enough, even if you don't look at the voltmeter," he grinned, "because all the lights will go dim and we'll start bumping into things."

"That's easy enough," said Grandma, "but what we need now is a cup of tea. I'll just put the kettle on."

"That will really test our power station," said Grandpa to Peter. "The kettle takes 3 kilowatts, that's a huge amount of electricity."

They watched the voltmeter. The needle quivered as she switched the kettle on, but steadied back at exactly 240 volts. Half a mile away, the water going over the waterwheel was boiling the kettle in the house.

"Free Tea!" cried Grandma, pouring it out.

"I'll make the toast," said Peter, putting some bread in the toaster.

"Free toast!" he shouted as it popped up.

"I feel a bit chilly," laughed Grandpa, turning on an electric heater.

"FREE!" they all shouted together.....

Change - Over Switch

An electric change-over switch is very similar to a set of points on a railway; diverting the electric current instead of the trains. There is a cable from the power station which carries the 'mains' electricity and another cable from the watermill (hydro). Each cable has two thick wires, one red and one black.

A change-over switch is used to select which source of electricity supplies the house. The switch has two metal switch 'blades' or 'contacts' which connect the house wiring to whichever supply is required.

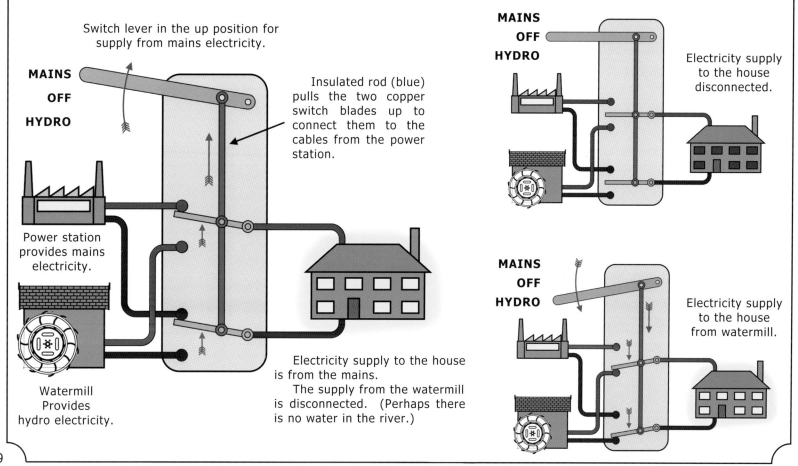

Switch lever in the up position for supply from mains electricity.

MAINS

OFF

HYDRO

Power station provides mains electricity.

Watermill Provides hydro electricity.

Insulated rod (blue) pulls the two copper switch blades up to connect them to the cables from the power station.

Electricity supply to the house is from the mains. The supply from the watermill is disconnected. (Perhaps there is no water in the river.)

MAINS

OFF

HYDRO

Electricity supply to the house disconnected.

MAINS

OFF

HYDRO

Electricity supply to the house from watermill.

The Steam Car (Mis)Adventure

One day they had an eccentric visitor.

Mr Gerry Mason had written to them saying he had heard of their railway and would love to see it. Would it be possible for him to drive over in his steam car for a visit? He would be delighted to take them all for rides in the car if that would amuse them.

"I expect it will be a rotten old contraption," said Peter while they were waiting for him to arrive. "I doubt it will even get to 30 miles an hour."

It was something of a surprise when Mr Mason drove up to the house. His steam car was a spectacular machine in every way. It had the most enormous bonnet, huge wire wheels and just two bucket seats perched high at the back – right beside the petrol tank.

This machine was clearly built for speed.

"Hello!" the driver shouted as he stopped and jumped down. "I'm Gerry. What do you think of the old girl? I got her up to seventy on the way here!"

After a bit of chat and a cup of tea, Gerry told them all about his car.

"She was made by the Stanley Steam Car Company in 1908, in America," he began. "And this type were known as the 'Vanderbilt Stanleys' as they were built to compete in the famous Vanderbilt Cup race. She's very powerful but the brakes are rubbish, which makes it even more exciting!"

The petrol burning boiler was under the bonnet and worked at 600 psi. It could get up steam in just ten minutes from cold.

"Amazing," said Grandpa. "Just think, Peter. That's five times the pressure which Fiery Fox runs on. And we take over an hour to get up steam."

Then Gerry Mason showed them the engine, underneath the car.

"There's no gearbox," he explained. "The engine drives the back wheels directly. They're more or less just stuck on the ends of the crankshaft."

Just then, Grandma came out to say hello and asked Mr Mason to stay for dinner. She was cooking a curry.

"How kind of you. Yes please," he replied. "Would you like to come for the first spin in the car?"

"I'd love to," she grinned and leapt up into the bucket seat.

Mr Mason jumped up beside her, pressed some buttons, pulled some levers, inspected the pressure gauge, shouted "600 psi!" and put his foot down on the accelerator.

With no observable effort, the car hissed a little and shot off down the road.

Grandma screamed in terror as they hurtled round the first bend.

"Ha Ha! Isn't it fun!" cried Mr Mason, as he pressed the accelerator harder into the floor.

"H..e..l..p..!" she screamed, as the car sped off towards the next bend. Poor Grandma.

And poor Mr Mason; he had made a dreadful mistake. He thought Grandma was enjoying the ride and just screaming like people do on roller-coasters, from the thrill of the speed.

By the time they got back to the farm, Grandma was white as a sheet and quite exhausted.

Mr Mason was really distressed. He hadn't meant to upset her at all and kept apologising.

"I'll be alright in a few minutes," she said rather weakly and went indoors to sit down.

Then it was time for Peter's run in the car. It was exhilarating and like nothing he had ever experienced. A steam car has no loud exhaust and no roaring engine. When Mr Mason put his foot on the accelerator, the car hissed and simply leapt forwards. It felt like a huge hand on Peter's back, pushing hard.

"The old girl does only 10 miles to the gallon of petrol," he told Peter, "and she uses a gallon of water every mile. But at least water is cheaper than petrol," he laughed.

After Grandpa's run, they took Gerry to the old barn. "Did I tell you that we too have a steam road vehicle?" asked Grandpa with a smile.

"It's not as fast as your car," added Peter as they threw open the doors to reveal Mighty Atom, their traction engine. "But she is very powerful, in a slow sort of way."

Gerry Mason was intrigued by the story of how they had found her, hidden away in the barn and how they had put her back to work again. He spent a long time looking at all her different parts and asking all sorts of questions.

But then it was time to show him the railway and the afternoon passed in a pleasant haze of steam, trains and good chat.

While they were outside playing trains, Grandma was inside, cooking the curry. She was still rather shaken from Mr Mason's terrible driving, when all of a sudden, she had a naughty idea. She giggled to herself as she added twice the amount of curry powder to his portion. It would be very, very hot...

Later on, poor Mr Mason had real difficulty eating it. He went bright red in the face and had to drink water between each mouthful, to try to put out the fire.

"I am so glad you like curry Mr Mason," said Grandma sweetly. "Would you like some more?"

Slowly it dawned on Mr Mason that Grandma had played a joke on him.

"Ha Ha!" he roared with laughter. "You've got your own back for my horrible driving this morning. Are we still friends?"

"Of course we are," smiled Grandma. "Now would you like something nice to eat? I made something else as well."

When they had finished eating, Gerry Mason told them a ridiculous story. It might even have been true....

"I know lots about steam cars," he explained, "but I only know one fact about railways. And it's totally useless. Would you like me to tell you?"

Of course they all wanted to hear it, so he started his story.

"The standard gauge or width of the tracks on British Railways is four feet, and eight and a half inches," he began.

"Yes, I knew that," said Grandpa. "But I always wondered why. It's such an exceedingly odd number."

"Well that's what my story is about," said Gerry. "It all depends on what units of measurement you use. If you use feet and inches it is very odd. But if you measure the width in Horses' Bums, it's much simpler."

"In fact," he went on, "railway lines in Britain are *exactly* two horses' bums wide!"

"You're pulling our legs," said Grandma, using another of her funny sayings. "How do you work that out?"

"You have to go back over 2000 years ago, when the Roman armies invaded Britain," he replied.

"They used chariots and wagons pulled by two horses, side by side. The shafts were just wide enough to fit beside the horses and the wheels were the same width again. Two horses' bums."

"Whatever has that got to do with railways?" asked Peter.

"I am coming to that," Gerry smiled. "The Romans built the original long distance roads and as they drove their chariots, the wheels wore long ruts or grooves in them. After that, everyone else had to use the same wheel spacing so their wagons would fit the ruts."

"Later, when engineers made the first tramways for moving coal, they just copied the road wagons. Later still, the engineers who built the first steam railways, just copied the tramways."

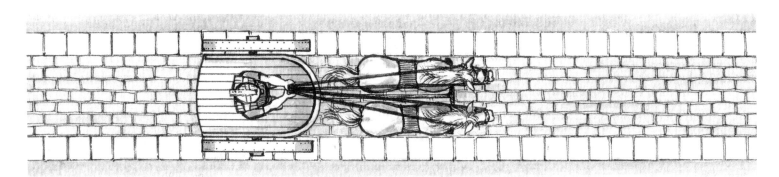

"So there you have it," he beamed. "The standard British Railway gauge is exactly two horses' bums!"

"It is certainly much easier to remember than four feet, eight and a half inches," laughed Grandpa.

"Or 1435 millimetres," added Peter, who was a bit more modern.

Soon it was time for Gerry to go home, so they all went outside to see him off.

The fire in the boiler lit with a pop and a flash and a few minutes later, steam was up.

Thanking them all for a wonderful time, Gerry Mason hissed off into the night.

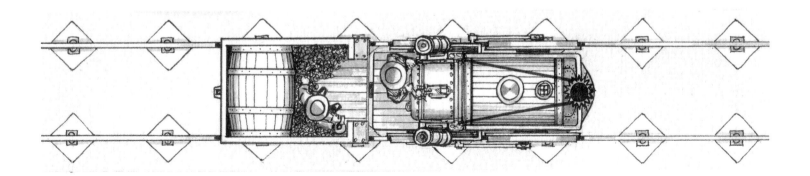

Railway to the Rescue

The watermill had been working for over a month now and there was plenty of water to keep it running. It was meant to be summer, but in true British tradition, it had been raining almost continuously for the last week.

"It's raining cats and dogs outside," said Grandma, coming in from a walk with Minnie. "I've never seen the river so high."

Just then the telephone rang and Grandma answered it. The call was from one of her friends who lived at Yockletts. Peter and Grandpa could only hear one end of the conversation, but it sounded serious.

"Oh hello Mary……. What a disaster……. Are you alright?……. Thank goodness for that…… Yes yes, of course you can come and stay here…… Bye for now…… and good luck…."

"The river has burst its banks at the village," she said when she'd put the phone down. "All the roads are under water and some of the houses are flooded. The water's still rising; it's a desperate situation."

"I told Mary she could bring her family to stay with us. And anyone else who's been flooded out. But with the roads under water I don't know how they're going to get here….."

"Come on Peter," interrupted Grandpa. "The railway's the only way to get them out. There's no time to lose. This is an emergency!"

Grandma drew up a plan with military precision.

She telephoned Colin at Woodland Cottage and asked him to go and buy lots of extra food. The nearest shop was in the village of Oaksted several miles away. Thankfully the roads between there and Woodland Cottage weren't flooded. The food would be picked up by the first train.

While on the phone, she asked if Jo and the twins could come up to the farm and help making beds and getting things ready. They could travel up on the first train with the food.

Meanwhile Peter and Grandpa were out in the engine shed, getting up steam. It seemed to take forever, especially as they were in such a hurry.

Eventually though, the pressure gauge showed working pressure and the tender was full of coal and water. They were ready for the mission.

With trucks, wagons and guard's van coupled on behind, Peter climbed onto Fiery Fox and eased her out of the shed and into the rain.

The first trip to Woodland Cottage was an easy run, downhill on the wet rails.

On the platform there was milk, bread, bottled water, biscuits and more. There was so much they would have to do several runs to carry it all. Colin, Jo, Kitty and Harry got on the train too, so they could help Grandma get ready for the invasion.

With a very full load, Peter set off round the loop and back towards the farm.

He had to be very careful with the regulator as the train was very heavy and the rails were wet and slippery. Too much steam and Fiery Fox's wheels spun hopelessly. With care though, he accelerated the train past the watermill and took a run at the long bank.

They lost speed up the hill, but made it slowly into the station at the farm. Jo, Colin and the twins got off and Peter set out again for Yockletts.

After the level crossing on the drive, the line drops quite quickly down to the front field by the river. Peter drove slowly down the gradient as it was more important to arrive safely than take risks and have a crash.

It was just as well, for as they came round the curve into the front field, they saw it was half flooded. The track simply disappeared under water.

"We'll never get though," shouted Peter to Grandpa, behind him.

"Just take it very slowly," Grandpa called back. "As long as the water is no higher than the grate in the firebox, you won't put the fire out. No racing though!"

Peter entered the flood at less than walking pace. Any faster and the waves under the engine would push water up into the fire.

"Easy does it old girl," he whispered to the engine, as if he was coaxing along a frightened horse.

Gliding through the water, the train looked like a very odd sort of boat. Ripples spread out like an arrow from the front of Fiery Fox as she cut her way through.

Once he realised he could get through the flood, Peter relaxed. It was only then that he noticed a funny regular sploshing noise.

'Whatever can it be?' he wondered to himself.

Looking along the side of the engine, he at once saw the coupling rods were dipping in and out of the water as they went round with the wheels. It was a most unusual sight and sound.

Giving a long blast on the whistle, they approached Yockletts station. Waiting for them there was a bedraggled bunch of people, including the headmistress from Peter's school.

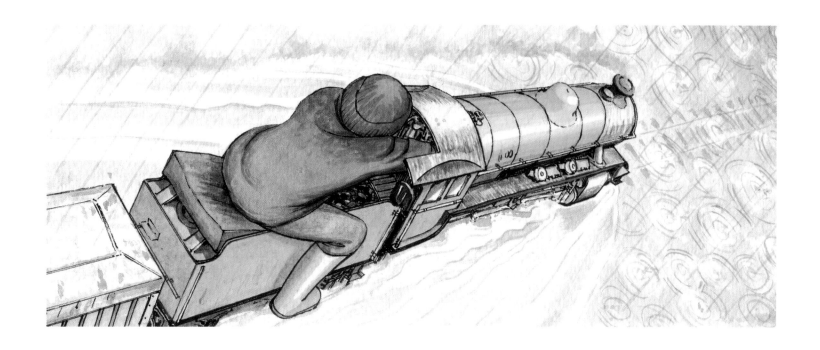

"Railway to the Rescue!" shouted Peter, as he pulled up at the platform.

The people who could stay in the village took away the food and provisions, it would keep them going for a few days at least. Those whose houses had flooded climbed onto the train to be taken to the farm. There were some cats and dogs too, which Peter loaded into the special animal wagons, to keep them safe on the journey.

It was a bit like Noah's Ark in the biblical flood, except that they couldn't all fit onto the train at once.

"Don't worry," Grandpa told them. "We'll come straight back again. We won't stop until we've got everyone."

Off they went, slowly at first, crawling through the water. Then as the line gained height, it lifted out of the flood. Peter opened up the regulator and gave Fiery Fox full steam to charge the bank.

Her wheels slipped a little, but she didn't stall and they arrived at Gerald's Cross station in fine style.

Grandma and the twins were standing on the platform to welcome them. Kitty ran to the engine and filled the tender with water and put some coal in the fire.

"We've got all the beds in the house made up," Grandma announced. "And lots of air beds and mattresses in the barn for you. I'm sorry it isn't as good as your own houses, but at least it's dry."

When everyone was off the train, including sundry cats and dogs, Peter and Grandpa set off again for Woodland Cottage. There were still more supplies to pick up for the stranded village, and more people to rescue. They ran train after train.

"Three Cheers for Fiery Fox!" everyone cried as the last train pulled into Gerald's Cross station. They were safe at last.

Peter and Grandpa were soaked to the skin and very tired by the time they put the engine away and let the fire down. But it had been a most satisfying day and the railway had been a lifeline.

In the barn, a big feast was cooking up and it was clear that some celebrations were in order.

When everyone had eaten, one of the men from the village got to his feet and made a speech.

"On behalf of us all," he began, "I would like to thank Peter and his family for rescuing us today. Without your railway I don't know what we would have done."

Everyone nodded and murmured their agreement.

"As a measure of our gratitude," he continued, "we would like to extend the honour of 'The Freedom of Yockletts Village' to Peter and his family."

"We were very pleased to help," replied Grandpa.

"And it was great fun too!" laughed Peter, with a grin from ear to ear.

The party went on with stories, jokes and gossip. When there was a lull in the conversation, Peter asked Grandpa if he would tell the story about 'Ocky' the cat.

"Well, it all happened a long time ago," Grandpa began, "when a stray cat took up residence at one of the railway stations in Manchester."

"This particular station was called 'Oxford Road' and the staff there named the cat 'Ocky', after the station."

"One day a diesel train arrived at the platform, just as Ocky was crossing the tracks. Although the driver braked as hard as he could, he still hit poor Ocky."

"Luckily for the cat, he was a kind man and leapt down from his cab and scooped up Ocky into his arms. He hadn't been killed, but he was quite badly injured."

"The driver then carried Ocky to the local vet and gave instructions to fix him up and send him the bill. He would pay it himself."

"Did he recover?" they all wanted to know.

"He certainly did," said Grandpa. "And that's the curious thing. Every time that driver stopped at Oxford Road station, on his regular duties, Ocky would come bounding down the platform and jump into his cab."

"Then he would keep the driver company, sitting on the control panel, all the way to Sheffield and back again to Oxford Road."

"He did the same thing every day for years, but he never jumped in with any other drivers." said Grandpa smiling as he thought about the lucky cat.

They were still talking about Ocky when Peter's headmistress came over.

"Have you got a minute?" she asked them both. "I've an idea which might be interesting for you."

"There are a lot of children who come to school from Oaksted," she explained. "It's quite a few miles beyond Woodland Cottage, and they all come by car. In most cases there's only one child in each car and it must waste a huge amount of fuel."

"Well I was wondering," she continued, "if you would ever think about extending your railway to Oaksted? You could operate a school train service in the mornings and afternoons. With all the children on one train, it would save loads of petrol. And there is an additional benefit: With your open carriages, everyone would be wide awake by the time they got to school!"

"What a fantastic idea," said Peter immediately. "It would be just like the Romney Hythe and Dymchurch: A proper public railway."

"Can we build it?" he asked, his face beaming with excitement. "Our railway would suddenly have a real purpose and be used every day."

"It's a great idea," agreed Grandpa after a pause. "But I'm not so sure. It's a long way to Oaksted. And it would be *very* expensive. You know, we would have to build a lot more track than we have already. It would be a huge undertaking."

"We'll have to give it some very serious thought. But not tonight...," he laughed. "It's time for bed."

It had been a long and exhausting day and, once in bed, Peter soon fell into a deep sleep and started to dream.

He and Grandpa were driving Fiery Fox along the new railway to Oaksted. But a strange thing had happened to them. They had become very small and were standing *inside* the cab. It was beautifully warm from the heat of the boiler.

Peter, sitting on one side of the cab, looked out of the window in front. He could see the track ahead, but the boiler seemed enormous and blocked out half of his view. He could only see straight ahead and to his left. It was quite different from normal when he looked over the top of Fiery Fox.

He had one hand on the regulator and an elbow on the open window ledge. The smell of the countryside at night, mixed with smoke and hot oil filled the cab. He was a proper engine driver.

The new track was so perfect that Peter found he could open the regulator more and more. Faster and faster they steamed through the night. Every time Grandpa put more coal in the firebox, he could see a maelstrom of heat, fire and flames inside.

Fiery Fox had turned into a magical machine. She surged along the track, swaying gently from side to side. Steam roared up her chimney like flying white breath. All her moving parts made a wonderful rhythmical sound which mingled with the ringing of steel wheels on steel rails.

Mile after mile they plunged along the track through the dimly lit countryside. They passed other farms, villages and several stations. There was nobody on the platforms; they were all asleep in their beds.

How fast were they going?

How far would they go?

Another village…. another farm…. another station…. They sped past them all.

More water in the boiler….

More coal on the fire….

Peter couldn't wait to build the new line.

But that is another story………

The End.

Driving an LNER B1 Locomotive

1 Boiler for making high pressure steam
2 Smokebox collects smoke and exhaust steam
3 Chimney to release smoke and exhaust steam
4 Dome for collecting dry steam from boiler
5 Driving wheels (6 off) to drive the locomotive
6 Bogie wheels (4 off) to carry some of the weight
7 Driver's cab
8 Driver with hand on regulator
9 Fireman trimming the coal
10 Regulator to control steam to the cylinders
11 Reverser for forward or reverse gear and linking up
12 Brake handle
13 Brake pressure gauge shows how hard the brakes are on
14 Handle to lower the fire grate to drop the fire out
15 Whistle handle
16 Steam pressure gauge for boiler
17 Steam chest p' gauge shows how hard engine is working
18 Water gauge shows water level in boiler
19 Firehole door, opened to put on more coal
20 Fire goes through tubes in the boiler to heat the water
21 Steam valve for injector to put water into boiler
22 Cylinder (2 off) contains piston which drives the wheels
23 Drain valves to release water from cylinders when cold
24 Crank converts push-pull motion of pistons to rotation
25 Connecting rod connects piston rod to crank
26 Coupling rod couples the driving wheels together
27 Crosshead guides the piston rod
28 Valve chest contains valve to control steam to cylinder
29 Valve gear controls the valves
30 Oil box (1 of many)
31 Tender for holding coal and water to supply the boiler
32 Coal bunker
33 Water tank
34 Tender wheels (6 off) to carry weight of tender
35 Tender springs (6 off) let wheels run on uneven track

Some Special Words

Amp or Ampere   See electric current.

Conductor   Material which conducts electricity.

Cylinder   Round and smooth tube which contains the piston. The cylinders and pistons are the parts of the locomotive where the energy in the steam is converted into the useful motion of the train.

Drain valves   (Cylinder drains) Valves to let water escape from the cylinders when they are cold.

Electric current   The flow of electrically charged particles in a circuit. Measured in amperes or amps for short. If electricity is thought of as water flowing through a pipe, the current is the quantity of water which flows per (or every) second.

Friction   The resistance to motion when one object slides over another and generates heat.

Fuse   Electrical device to protect a circuit from too large a current. It has a thinner wire than the cable in the circuit so that it will 'blow' before the main circuit overheats.

Gradient   A slope or hill. On a railway only gentle gradients are used, up to about 1 in 50.

Hack saw   Saw for cutting metal.

Hydraulics   The use of very high pressure oil (or water) to operate machines. Either by pushing pistons (called rams in hydraulics) or by turning special motors.

Hydro electricity   Electricity made from falling or flowing water.

Insulator   Material which does not conduct electricity.

Mass   Quantity of matter in an object, measured in kilograms. Mass is what makes an object want to continue moving, (or remain stopped). Mass resists changes in motion. (Note, mass is <u>not</u> the same as weight.)

Momentum   A moving object contains momentum. The greater its mass and/or velocity, the greater its momentum.

Power   The rate at which mechanical work is done or energy converted from one form to another. Power is measured in watts. (some people measure power in 'horsepower'.)

Pulley	A wheel on a shaft for driving or being driven by an endless drive belt.
Pressure	When a lot of steam is squashed into a closed space, its pressure rises. Pressure is often measured in 'pounds per square inch' (or 'psi' for short).
	A pressure of 100 pounds per square inch means that on every square inch of the boiler shell or piston, the steam is pressing with a force of 100 pounds. A square inch is about 6 square centimetres or the area of a 10 pence coin. 100 pounds is about 40 kilograms or probably the weight of a young person. (The metric or proper unit of pressure is the 'newton per square metre' or 'pascal'. A newton is a force equal to the weight (on earth) of about one tenth of a kilogram. 100,000 pascals is called one 'bar' and one bar is equal to about 15 psi in old units. So 100 psi, the working pressure of Fiery Fox, is equal to a pressure of 6.5 bar.)
Pressure gauge	Device in the locomotive cab which shows the steam pressure in the boiler.
Regulator	Main steam valve used by the driver to control how much steam is used in the cylinders. The more the regulator is opened, the harder and faster the locomotive works. (The regulator is often called the throttle in America.)
Steam	When water boils it bubbles and turns into steam. Normally steam has a huge volume compared to the water it came from. However in the boiler it is contained in a closed space and so instead of expanding to a large volume, it rises in pressure.
Volt	Measure of the force of electricity or 'electromotive force' (e.m.f. for short). It is this electric force which pushes the electric current round a circuit. If electricity is thought of as water flowing in a pipe, the voltage would be the water pressure in the pipe which forces the water to move.
Water gauge	Device in the locomotive cab which shows the water level in the boiler.
Watt	Measure of the power of something. 1000 watts is called 1 kilowatt.
Weight	The downward pull or force of gravity on an object is its weight. Weight is not the same as mass. If you take an object with a mass of 1 kg (kilogram) to the moon, it will still have a mass of 1 kg and will resist acceleration the same as it does on earth. However its weight will be much less because gravity on the moon is much less.
Welding	Joining metal together by melting it to form a joint. Extra 'filler' metal is often added.

The Boiler - How the Locomotive Makes its Steam

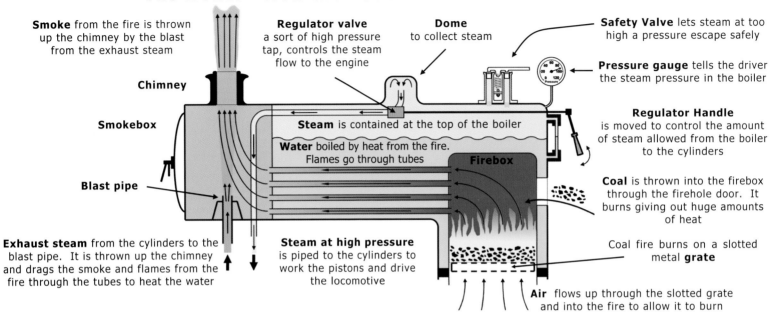

Smoke from the fire is thrown up the chimney by the blast from the exhaust steam

Chimney

Smokebox

Blast pipe

Exhaust steam from the cylinders to the blast pipe. It is thrown up the chimney and drags the smoke and flames from the fire through the tubes to heat the water

Regulator valve a sort of high pressure tap, controls the steam flow to the engine

Dome to collect steam

Steam is contained at the top of the boiler

Water boiled by heat from the fire. Flames go through tubes

Firebox

Steam at high pressure is piped to the cylinders to work the pistons and drive the locomotive

Safety Valve lets steam at too high a pressure escape safely

Pressure gauge tells the driver the steam pressure in the boiler

Regulator Handle is moved to control the amount of steam allowed from the boiler to the cylinders

Coal is thrown into the firebox through the firehole door. It burns giving out huge amounts of heat

Coal fire burns on a slotted metal **grate**

Air flows up through the slotted grate and into the fire to allow it to burn

Pistons and Cylinders - How the Steam Drives the Locomotive

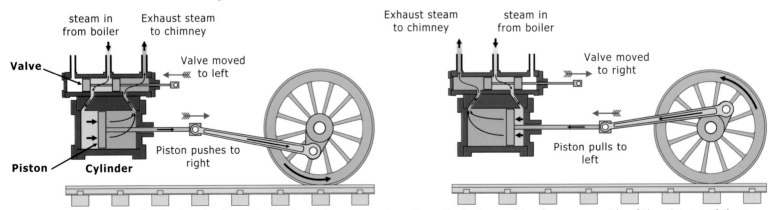

steam in from boiler

Exhaust steam to chimney

Valve moved to left

Valve

Piston pushes to right

Piston   **Cylinder**

Exhaust steam to chimney

steam in from boiler

Valve moved to right

Piston pulls to left

The piston pushes and pulls the wheel round with the high pressure steam from the boiler pushing first on one side of the piston and then on the other. The steam is let in and out of alternate ends of the cylinder by the valve which is moved automatically by the valve gear.